I HAVE ANOTHER NAME, A "SECRET IDENTITY" IF YOU WILL-- BUT THIS STADIUM OF SCREAMING FANS KNOWS ME AS
BAD BUNNY

IF YOU DON'T KNOW WHO I AM YET, YOU'RE IN THE MINORITY. LAST YEAR, SPOTIFY REVEALED THAT I WAS THE MOST POPULAR RECORDING ARTIST ON THEIR SERVICE.

IN DECEMBER ALONE, FANS STREAMED MY SONGS MORE THAN SIX HUNDRED MILLION TIMES ON YOUTUBE.

BUT BEFORE ALL THAT...

CHAPTER ONE: BAD BUNNY BEGINS

MUSIC WAS ALWAYS A PART OF MY LIFE.

WHEN I WAS A LITTLE KID, MY MOM WOULD PLAY THE OLD-SCHOOL LATIN CROONERS ON THE RADIO WHILE SHE WORKED.

I WOULD SING ALONG, TRYING TO IMPRESS HER.
♫♬ "HERE AND NOW LET'S GET THIS STRAIGHT. BOOGALOO BABY I MADE IT GREAT--"♫♬

♫♬ "--BECAUSE I GAVE IT THE LATIN BEAT!".♫♬
SHE WAS MY FIRST AUDIENCE.

...AND SHE INSTILLED IN ME THE CONFIDENCE I NEEDED TO PERFORM FOR A SLIGHTLY LARGER CROWD.

I PERFORMED IN THE CHURCH CHOIR FOR YEARS.
THE EXPERIENCE WAS INVALUABLE. I LEARNED ALL ABOUT DEVELOPING A WORK ETHIC, COLLABORATING WITH OTHER ARTISTS, AND EVEN A LITTLE BIT ABOUT HOW TO PRODUCE AUDIO.

THAT'S OUR BOY.
SNIFF
LOOK AT OUR LITTLE "BAD BUNNY!"

HOLD UP. I SHOULD PROBABLY EXPLAIN THE WHOLE "BAD BUNNY" NAME...
YEARS AGO:
STAY OUT
NO. I'M NOT COMING OUT.

BUDDY. COME ON OUT. I'M SURE IT LOOKS FINE...
SNICKER
KNOCK
KNOCK

WHEN I WAS A KID, ONE OF MY RELATIVES BOUGHT ME A BUNNY-THEMED PAIR OF PAJAMAS.
I HATED THEM WITH A BURNING PASSION.

HA HA HA HA HA HA
HA HA HA HA HA
GASP!
THEY LOOKS GREAT, REALLY!
GRRR...

CLICK
MY MOM TOOK A PHOTO OF ME IN THEM, AND I LOOKED LIKE A NIGHTMARE VERSION OF THE EASTER BUNNY.

SHE WROTE ON THE POLAROID...
OUR LITTLE BAD BUNNY
AND THE NICKNAME STUCK.
(YOU KNOW HOW LATINO FAMILIES ARE)

AFTER THE CHOIR RECITAL:
PER SIGNUM

HEY, WHAT IS THAT MUSIC?

WHAT-- YOU NEVER HEARD REGGAETON BEFORE?
I HADN'T.

BUT LATER, AT HOME, I FELL DOWN A "RABBIT" HOLE-- USING THE FAMILY COMPUTER TO LOOK UP EVERY REGGAETON ARTIST I COULD FIND.

A FEW YEARS LATER, REGGAETON WAS MY LIFE. NOT ONLY DID I LISTEN TO IT CONSTANTLY...
SUPERMERCADO
ECONOS

I MADE SURE EVERYONE AROUND ME DID TOO.

GET OFF THE INTERCOM!
ECONOS

BUMP
OOF!

WHEN I WASN'T CAUSING A RUCKUS AT MY GROCERY STORE DAY JOB, I GOT BUSY MAKING MY OWN MUSIC. I TAUGHT MYSELF HOW TO MAKE BEATS, USING PROGRAMS AND TUTORIALS I FOUND ON THE INTERNET.
TEC TEC TEC

AND I UPLOADED THE RESULTS OF MY EFFORTS FOR FREE ON WEBSITES LIKE SOUNDCLOUD.
UPLOAD
CLICK

HMM. GOTTA ENTER A SCREEN NAME TO UPLOAD THE MUSIC UNDER...
HA! I GOT IT!

BAD BUN

CHAPTER TWO: SOUNDCLOUD 9 & TRAPPING FAME IN PUERTO RICO

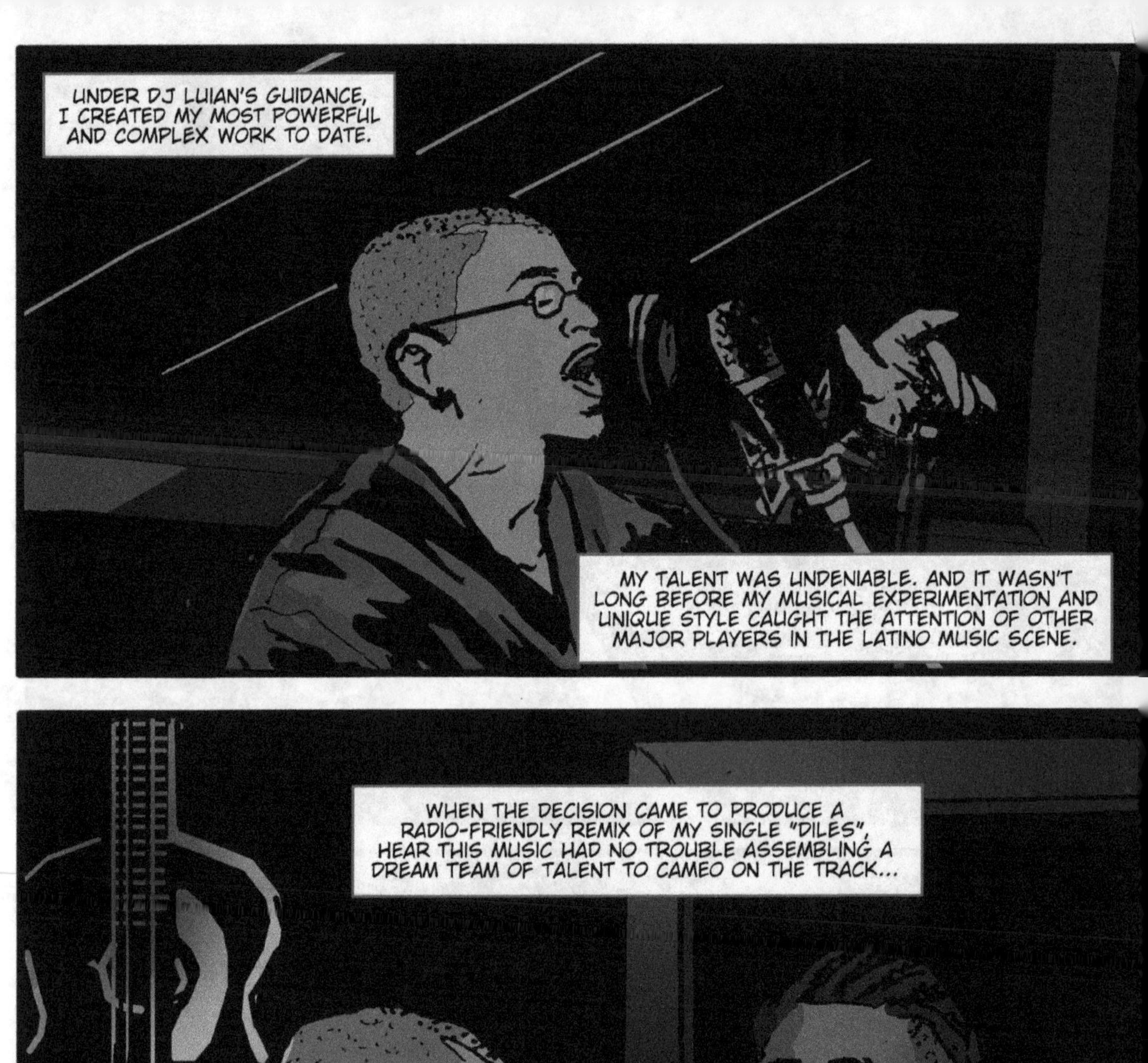
UNDER DJ LUIAN'S GUIDANCE, I CREATED MY MOST POWERFUL AND COMPLEX WORK TO DATE.
MY TALENT WAS UNDENIABLE. AND IT WASN'T LONG BEFORE MY MUSICAL EXPERIMENTATION AND UNIQUE STYLE CAUGHT THE ATTENTION OF OTHER MAJOR PLAYERS IN THE LATINO MUSIC SCENE.

WHEN THE DECISION CAME TO PRODUCE A RADIO-FRIENDLY REMIX OF MY SINGLE "DILES", HEAR THIS MUSIC HAD NO TROUBLE ASSEMBLING A DREAM TEAM OF TALENT TO CAMEO ON THE TRACK...
EMERGING REGGAETONEROS, LIKE OZUNA...

AS WELL AS OLD HEADS,
LIKE ARCÁNGEL...

FARRUKO...

AND ÑENGO FLOW.

IN THE SUMMER OF 2017, I INKED A BOOKING DEAL WITH THE CARDENAS MARKETING NETWORK, TO DO A TOUR OF LATIN AMERICA.
PEOPLE CAME OUT IN DROVES TO SEE ME. THEY PACKED STADIUMS.
CONCERT
WE LOVE YOU, BAD BUNNY!
'PPRECIATE YOU.
IT WAS A FAR CRY FROM FREE-STYLING OVER GROCERY STORE INTERCOMS.

BUT MY FIRST TOUR WAS CUT SHORT WHEN TRAGEDY STRUCK MY HOMELAND.
--AS HURRICANE IRMA RAVAGES PUERTO RICO...

IT WAS LIKE SOMETHING OUT OF A NIGHTMARE. FIRST HURRICANE IRMA. THEN, TWO WEEKS LATER, HURRICANE MARIA.
I USED THE MONEY I MADE ON TOUR TO HELP PURCHASE OOD, WATER AND GENERATORS FOR PEOPLE WHO WERE IN NEED.

I CAME HOME, AND PITCHED IN WHEREVER AND HOWEVER I COULD.
THANK YOU.
MY PLEASURE, MA'AM.
IT WAS THE LEAST I COULD DO.

I SOON FOUND MYSELF BECOMING AN OUTSPOKEN ADVOCATE FOR MY PEOPLE, USING MY NEWFOUND FAME TO ATTRACT ATTENTION TO ISSUES THAT ARE IMPORTANT TO ME.

THAT INCLUDES BEING AT ALLY TO LGQBT+ FOLKS-- A COMMUNITY THAT HAS BEEN TRADITIONALLY DISRESPECTED BY THE LATIN MUSIC SCENE.
I THINK, AS A REGGAETON SINGER, I HAVE A FAN BASE THAT NEEDS THAT KIND OF MESSAGE, OR THAT TYPE OF EDUCATION... LOVE IS LOVE.

I'M TRYING TO LIVE MY LIFE IN A WAY THAT INSPIRED THE NEXT GENERATION OF YOUNG MEN TO REJECT THE LONG HISTORY OF APATHY, MACHISMO AND HOMOPHOBIA THAT PLAGUES OUR CULTURE.
OHMYGOD OHMYGOD OHMY--

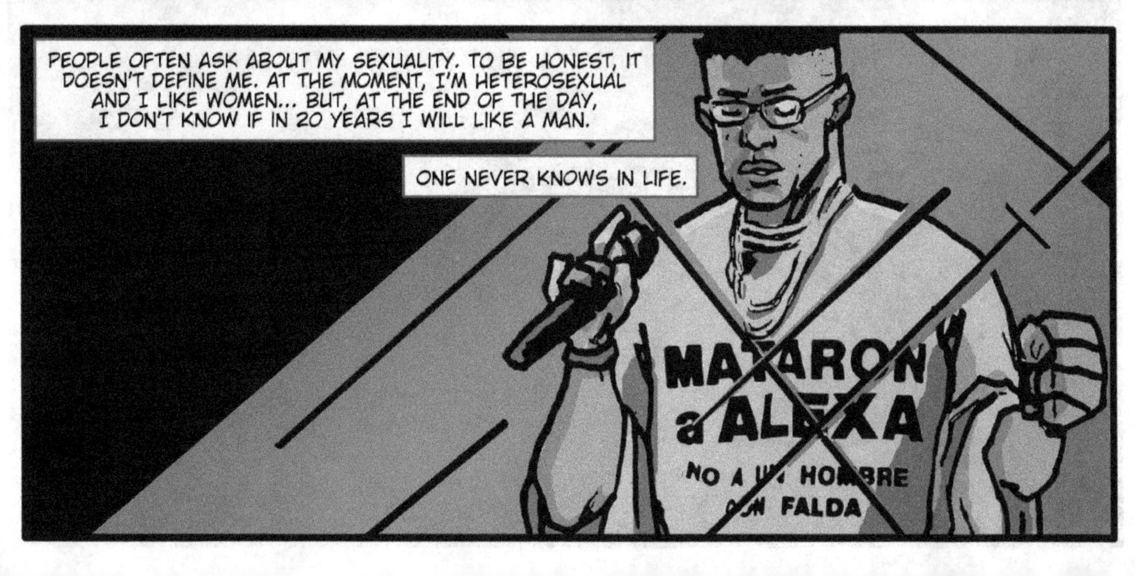
PEOPLE OFTEN ASK ABOUT MY SEXUALITY. TO BE HONEST, IT DOESN'T DEFINE ME. AT THE MOMENT, I'M HETEROSEXUAL AND I LIKE WOMEN... BUT, AT THE END OF THE DAY, I DON'T KNOW IF IN 20 YEARS I WILL LIKE A MAN.
ONE NEVER KNOWS IN LIFE.
MATARON a ALEXA

X 100PRE WAS MY FIRST WHOLE ALBUM.
THE RECORD RECEIVED RAVE REVIEWS FROM THE LATIN AMERICAN MUSIC SCENE...
HEY, WHAT ARE YOU GUYS PLAYING RIGHT NOW? IT'S AMAZING!
MEXICO CITY, MEXICO
AND, TO MY SURPRISE, DID JUST AS WELL WITH SPANISH-SPEAKING MUSIC LOVERS LIVING IN DIASPORA IN THE STATES.
Amoeba Music
LOS ANGELES, CALIFORNIA

IT'S THE NEW BAD BUNNY RECORD. PRETTY GREAT, RIGHT?

X 100PRE WON "BEST URBAN ALBUM" AT THE 2019 LATIN GRAMMYS.
THERE'S SO MANY THINGS TO SAY. I KNOW THEY'RE PROBABLY GOING TO CUT ME OFF. SCREW THEM. BUT TO ALL THE MUSICIANS, TO ALL THE PEOPLE WHO BELONG TO THE ACADEMY...

WITH ALL MY RESPECTS, REGGAETON IS PART OF LATIN CULTURE, AND IT'S REPRESENTING--JUST LIKE LOTS OF OTHER MUSIC GENRES--LATINOS AROUND THE WORLD.

ALSO, I TELL MY COLLEAGUES FROM REGGAETON, LET'S MAKE AN EFFORT; LET'S BRING BACK CREATIVITY AND SINCERITY. THE GENRE HAS BECOME ABOUT VIEWS, NUMBERS. LET'S TURN THINGS AROUND AND DO GENUINE THINGS AND UNIQUE THINGS FOR THE PEOPLE.

CLAP
CLAP
CLAP
CLAP

CHAPTER THREE: WORLDWIDE FAME

WHEN I DRESSED IN DRAG FOR MY NEXT BIG SINGLE, YO PERREO SOLA, IT CAPTURED PEOPLES' ATTENTION IN A BIG WAY...

MAKING HEADLINES ACROSS THE WORLD.
News
Bad Bunny Shocks Fans
Notíc
Bad Bunny deixa fãs chocad

CLICK
DO I LIKE BAD BUNNY? OF COURSE I DO! I THINK HE'S A LQBTQ+ ICON, WHO IS CHANGING THE LANDSCAPE OF LATIN MUSIC.
WHEN JOURNALISTS ASKED RICKY MARTIN-- ANOTHER LATINO ICON, WHO MANAGED TO FIND FANS IN BOTH THE SPANISH AND ENGLISH LANGUAGE MARKETS-- WHAT HE THOUGHT OF MY WORK, HE WAS INCREDIBLY KIND.

ALL OF THAT ATTENTION RESULTED IN THE BIGGEST OPPORTUNITY IN MY CAREER TO DATE...
IN FEBRUARY OF 2020, I PERFORMED TO THE LARGEST AUDIENCE OF MY CAREER-- AT THE NFL'S SUPER BOWL HALFTIME SHOW.

AND I WASN'T ALONE. I WAS JOINED BY LEGENDS:

SHAKIRA.

JENNIFER LOPEZ

AND THE HOMIE, J. BALVIN.

I'M TOLD THAT AFTER THE GAME "WHO IS BAD BUNNY?" WAS ONE OF THE MOST GOOGLED QUESTIONS OF THE YEAR.

THE NEWFOUND ATTENTION FROM THE SUPER BOWL LED TO A ROLLING STONE COVER.
THE ACCOMPANYING ARTICLE WAS THE FIRST EVER TO BE WRITTEN AND SHOT COMPLETELY BY LATINAS.
THE ARTICLE WAS WRITTEN BY SUZY EXPOSITO.
BRAVOS
BAD BUNNY

PEOPLE THINK I'M SPENDING QUARANTINE IN A HUGE MANSION, WITH A REALLY AWESOME POOL ... BUT I'M JUST STUCK IN MY APARTMENT, WATCHING THE TOY STORY MOVIES ON REPEAT...
THAT'S GREAT. THAT'S DEFINITELY GOING IN THE ARTICLE.

AND THE PHOTOS WERE SHOT BY GABRIELA BELENGERI-- MY GIRLFRIEND, AND QUARANTINE HOUSEMATE.

MANY PEOPLE HAVE SAID THAT IT WAS ONE OF THE MOST INTIMATE SHOOTS EVER FEATURED IN THE MAGAZINE.

ARE YOU SURE I LOOK COOL?
THE COOLEST.

I'M A BUSY GUY. BUT I DON'T THINK I'LL KEEP THIS PACE FOREVER.
SIGH.

IF YOU'RE A FAN, YOU'VE ALREADY PICKED UP THE HINTS.
♫♬ "PERO HABLANDO CLARO, GENTE, YA NI DUERMO. Y ESTO DE LA FAMA ME TIENE HASTA ENFERMO..."* ♫♬
DOES THAT MEAN WHAT I THINK IT MEANS?
♫♬ *"BUT SPEAKING CLEARLY, PEOPLE, I DON'T EVEN SLEEP ANYMORE. AND THIS THIS FAME THING HAS ME SICK." ♫♬

HONESTLY, I HAVE NO IDEA WHAT'S NEXT FOR ME.
BUT I KNOW THAT WHATEVER COMES, I'LL HAVE THE SUPPORT OF MY PEOPLE BEHIND ME.

THE GLOBAL PANDEMIC MADE IT IMPOSSIBLE TO TOUR IN 2020.
UGH. I AM SO BORED.
... SO I FOCUSED ON MY MUSIC, AND PUT OUT THREE RECORDS IN A SINGLE YEAR...

YHLQMDLG
LAS QUE NO IBAN A SALIR
AND EL ÚLTIMO TOUR DEL MUNDO.
SIGH.

I EVEN TOOK A GIG DOING A HOT CHEETOS COMMERCIAL, JUST TO GET OUT OF THE HOUSE.
WELL... AND BECAUSE I GOT TO MEET CHESTER THE CHEETAH.

... AND BECAUSE THE CHEETO CORPORATION PROMISED TO DONATE $500,000 TO MY "GOOD BUNNY FOUNDATION", TO PROVIDE SUPPORT FOR THE HISPANIC COMMUNITY.

I'VE ALSO DIPPED MY TOE INTO THE ACTING POOL RECENTLY, TAKING A GUEST SPOT AS ARTURO "KITTY" PAEZ ON NARCOS: MEXICO.
NARCOS
MEXICO

...AND PERFORMING AS A LARGER-THAN-LIFE VERSION OF MYSELF WITH THE WWE.

Eric Esquivel & Amanda Del Cid Lugo — Writer

Victor Moura — Art

Benjamin Glibert — Letters

Darren G. Davis — Editor

Joe Phillips — Cover

Special Thanks: Oscar Valentín Del Cid & Paola Nicole Lugo

Darren G. Davis
Publisher

Maggie Jessup
Publicity

Susan Ferris
Entertainment Manager

Steven Diggs Jr.
Marketing Manager

CPSIA information can be obtained
at www.ICGtesting.com
Printed in the USA
BVHW011342191021
619306BV00012B/340